Level K

Lesley Mandel Morrow
Senior Author

Marie Garman   Patricia Maureen Mount   Patricia Scanlon

~~~~~~ Literacy Consultants ~~~~~~

Heather K. Casey, Ph.D.
Department of Teacher Education
Rider University

Ernest Morrell, Ph.D.
Graduate School of Education
University of California, Los Angeles

Jennifer Rowsell, Ph.D.
Graduate School of Education
Rutgers University

Erica C. Boling, Ph.D.
Graduate School of Education
Rutgers University

Robert Calfee, Ph.D.
Graduate School of Education
University of California, Riverside

Robert Rueda, Ph.D.
Rossier School of Education
University of Southern California

Carmelita Williams, Ed.D.
Graduate School of Education
Norfolk State University

Cheryl Dyer
Assistant Superintendent
Bridgewater-Raritan (NJ) School District

Eleanor M. Vargas
Teacher Education Department
Claremont Graduate University

Diane H. Tracey, Ed.D.
College of Education
Kean University

D. Ray Reutzel, Ph.D.
Emma Eccles Jones College of Education
and Human Services
Utah State University

Printed in the United States of America.   ISBN: 978-0-8215-7900-8   18 19 20 21 22 WEBC 25 24 23 22 21

Contents

RIDES

I ride on a bus.
I ride on a train.
I ride on a trolley.
I ride on a plane.

I ride on a ferry.
I ride in a car.
I ride on my skates—
But not very far.

But, best of all,
The ride I like
Is 'round the block
On my new bike.

Ilo Orleans

Oral Language Which rides are fast? Which rides are slow?
Which rides do you like? Why?

Name _____

Dear Family,

In this unit about transportation, your child will distinguish, identify, and manipulate sounds in spoken words. These skills improve children's ability to read words. You can enjoy learning with your child by trying these activities at home.

• Talk about the pictures below. Say their names aloud. Point out to your child that all of the picture names rhyme—or sound the same at the end. Can you think of other words that rhyme?

Apreciada Familia:

En esta unidad, que trata sobre el transporte, su niño distinguirá, identificará y manipulará el sonido en las palabras. Estas destrezas mejoran la capacidad del niño para leer palabras. Usted puede disfrutar el aprender con su hijo al hacer estas actividades en casa.

• Comenten los dibujos. Pronuncien los nombres en voz alta. Indique a su niño que los nombres de todas las imágenes riman— o suenan igual en la terminación. ¿Pueden pensar en otras palabras que rimen?

 **van**  **pan**  **fan**  **can**  **man**

• Read the poem "Rides" on the reverse side of this page to your child.

• Ask your child about the vehicles in the poem. Say their names slowly and ask your child to listen to the sounds that make up each word.

• Ask your child to listen as you read the poem aloud again. Then find the words in the poem that rhyme. **(train/plane, car/far, like/bike)**

• Lea el poema "Rides" en la página 5.

• Pregunte a su niño sobre los vehículos que se mencionan en el poema. Diga los nombres lentamente y pídale que escuche los sonidos que forman cada palabra.

• Pida a su niño que escuche mientras usted lee el poema en voz alta de nuevo. Después, encuentren las palabras que riman. **(train/plane, car/far, like/bike)**

PROJECT

With your child, make a list of vehicles, such as **van, train, car, plane,** and **bus.** Keep the list with you the next time you are out, and add to it as you see or hear words that rhyme with the words on your list.

PROYECTO

Con su niño, hagan una lista de vehículos. Lleve la lista la próxima vez que salgan y agreguen palabras que lean o escuchen y que rimen con las de la lista.

Name_____

DIRECTIONS: **Listen** to each sentence. **Print** an **X** on a wagon for each word that you hear. (Refer to page 7 in the Teacher's Edition.)

DIRECTIONS: **Say** the name of each picture. **Circle** the picture if its name rhymes with the name of the picture at the beginning of the row.

PHONICS ALIVE AT HOME   Name a picture, for example, **boat.** Together, think of rhyming words. **(coat, float, goat)**

Name_____

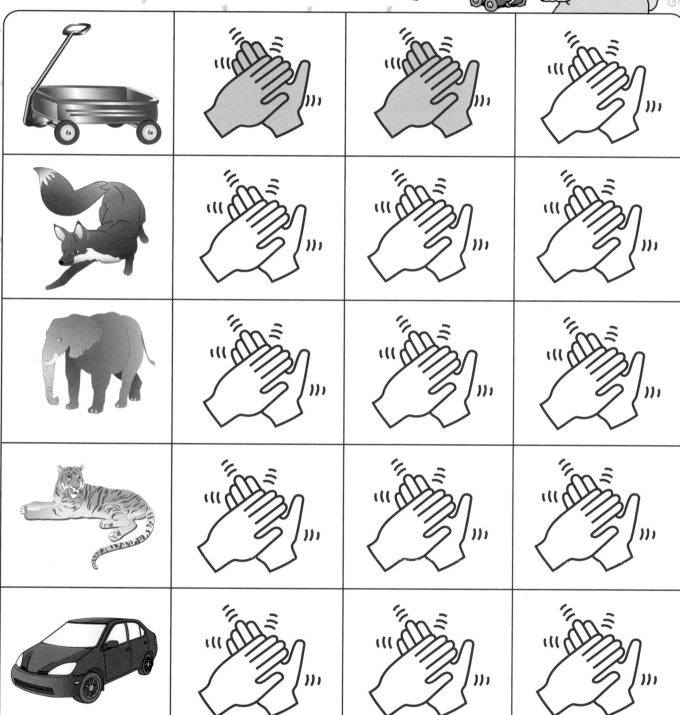

DIRECTIONS: **Say** the name of each picture. **Clap** the number of beats, or syllables, in the picture name. **Color** a pair of clapping hands for each beat that you hear.

DIRECTIONS: **Say** the names of the pictures on the vehicles in each row. **Circle** the picture whose name begins with **/v/** in Row 1, **/k/** in Row 2, **/m/** in Row 3, and **/j/** in Row 4.

PHONICS ALIVE AT HOME

Point to a picture and have your child say its name. Then ask him or her to tell you the beginning sound in the picture name.

Name_____

DIRECTIONS: **Say** the names of the pictures on each rocket. For rockets 1 and 2, **color** the pictures whose names begin with the same sound. For rockets 3 and 4, **color** the pictures whose names end with the same sound.

Lesson 6 • Phonemic Awareness: Phoneme Matching

DIRECTIONS: **Say** the name of each picture. **Draw** an **X** on the picture in each row that begins with a different sound than the other two.

PHONICS ALIVE AT HOME

Point to the two pictures in Row 1 that begin with the same sound. Ask your child to name another word that begins with that sound. Repeat for remaining rows.

Name_____

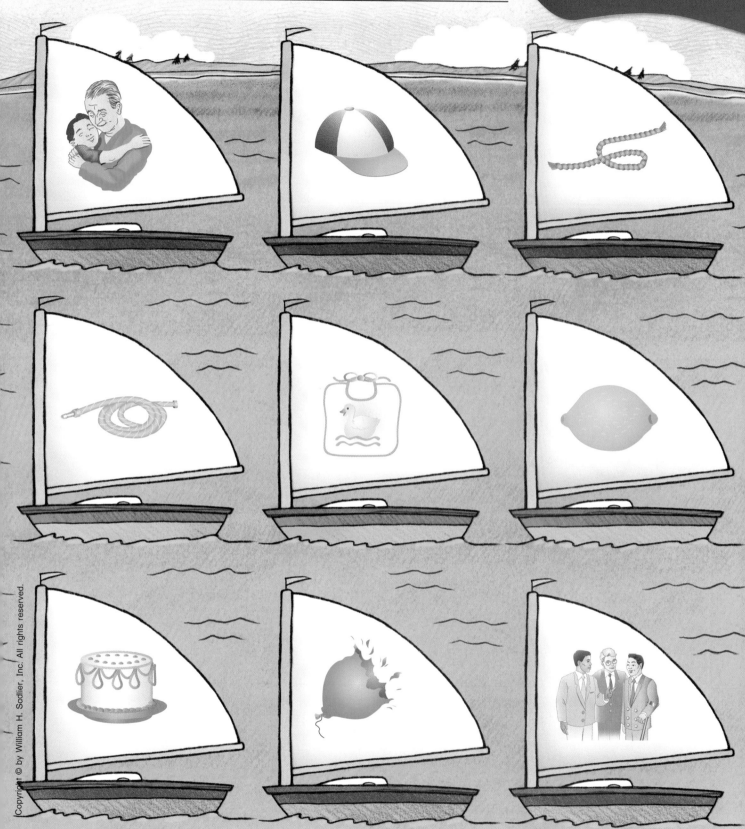

DIRECTIONS: **Say** the name of the pictures in each row. **Circle** the picture for **/h/-/u/-/g/** in Row 1, **/b/-/i/-/b/** in Row 2, and **/m/-/e/-/n/** in Row 3.

Phoneme Segmentation

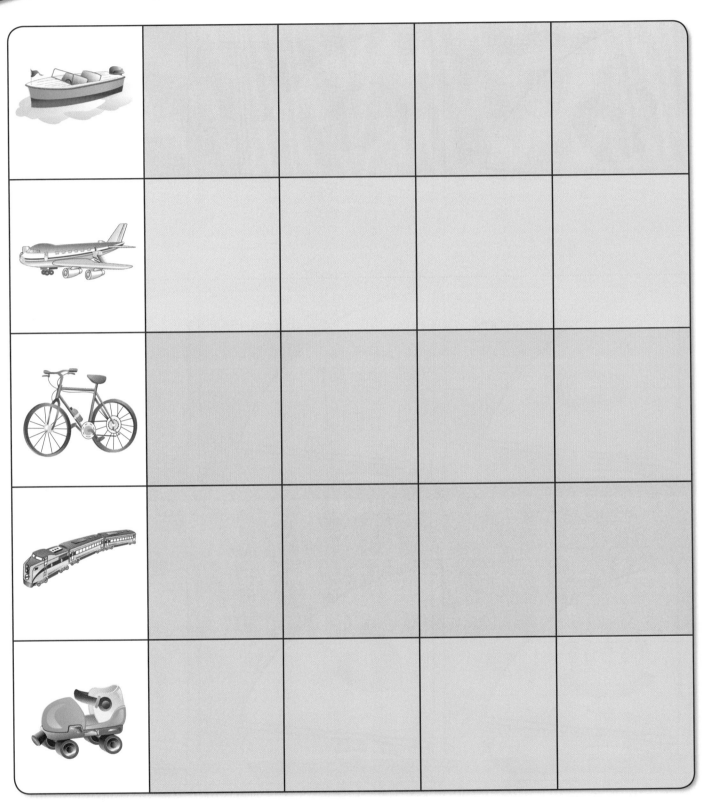

⭐ DIRECTIONS: **Say** the name of the picture at the beginning of each row. **Print** an **X** in a box for each sound you hear.

14 **Lesson 8** • Phonemic Awareness: Phoneme Segmentation

PHONICS ALIVE AT HOME Say a few short words such as **cab, skate, ride,** and **stop.** Ask your child to repeat the word and count the number of sounds he or she hears.

Name_____

DIRECTIONS: **Say** the name of the picture at the beginning of each row. In Row 1, what is **snail** without /s/? **Circle** your answer. In Row 2, what is **leg** without /l/? **Circle** your answer. In Row 3, what is **box** without /b/? **Circle** your answer. In Row 4, what is **train** without /t/? **Circle** your answer.

Phoneme Addition

DIRECTIONS: **Say** the name of the picture at the beginning of each row. In Row 1, what word do you have if you add **/f/** to the beginning of **ox?** **Circle** your answer. Add **/b/** to **ride** in Row 2. Add **/w/** to **ax** in Row 3. Add **/k/** to **lock** in Row 4. **Circle** your answers.

16   Lesson 9 • Phonemic Awareness:
       Phoneme Addition

PHONICS ALIVE AT HOME

Say the following words and have your child add an **s** sound to the beginning of each word and say the new word: **mile** (smile), **led** (sled), **team** (steam), **lip** (slip).

Name_____

Phoneme Substitution

Copyright © by William H. Sadlier, Inc. All rights reserved.

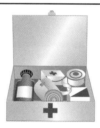

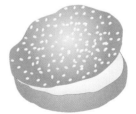

DIRECTIONS: **Say** the name of the first picture in each row. In Row 1, change /n/ to /j/. **What word do you get? Circle** your answer. In Row 2, change /k/ to /h/. In Row 3, change /f/ to /p/. In Row 4, change /b/ to /t/. **Circle** your answers.

Lesson 10 • Phonemic Awareness: Phoneme Substitution

17

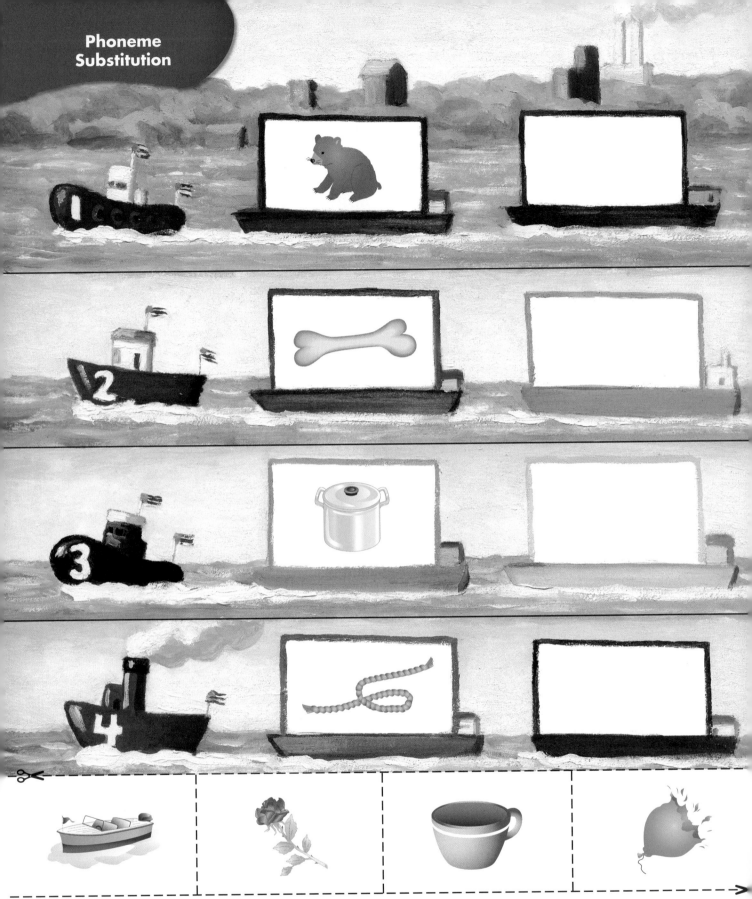

DIRECTIONS: Cut out the pictures at the bottom. **Say** the name of the picture on the first boat: **cub.** Change final **/b/** to **/p/.** What's the new word? **Glue** its picture on the empty boat. For the second boat, change **/n/** in **bone** to **/t/.** For the third boat, change **/t/** in **pot** to **/p/.** For the fourth boat, change **/p/** in **rope** to **/z/. Glue** the correct pictures on the empty boats.

Name _____

 DIRECTIONS: Aa go together. The big letter is called the capital letter. The capital and small letters on each car go together. Look at the letters on each car. **Sing** "The Alphabet Song" as you point to each letter on pages 19 and 20.

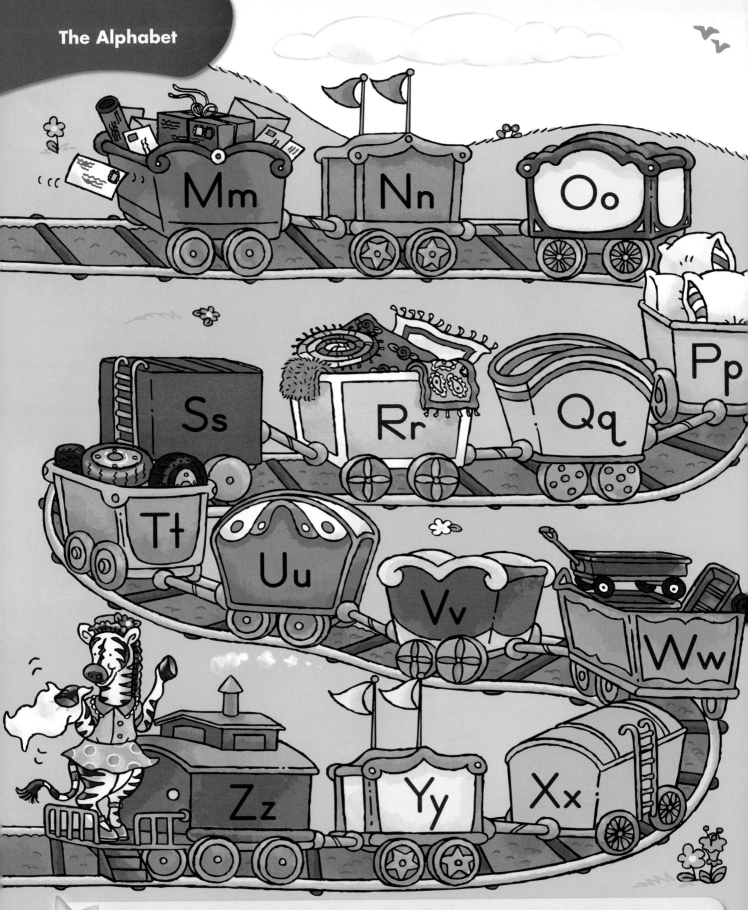

DIRECTIONS: **Look** at the letters on pages 19 and 20 again. **Circle** any letters that are in your first and last name.

 PHONICS ALIVE AT HOME

With your child, list the names of family members. Point to a letter on your list and ask your child to find the same letter on the train.

Happy Birthday to Me!

My piñata is hanging
from my favorite tree.
Is it full of surprises
for friends and for me?

I'm happy, as happy,
as happy can be!
¡Feliz Cumpleaños!
Happy Birthday to me!

Carmen Muñoz

Oral Language How is your birthday special?
How have you changed this year?

Name _____

Dear Family,

In this unit, your child will talk about ways everyone is special. She or he will also learn the sounds of **f, m, s, t, h,** and **b** at the beginning of words. You can try these activities at home.

• Look at the pictures below. Say each letter and picture name with your child. Listen to the beginning consonant sound in each word.

Apreciada Familia:

En esta unidad a su niño se le hablará de que todos somos especiales. También aprenderá los sonidos de la **f, m, s, t, h** y la **b** al principio de una palabra. Pueden hacer estas actividades en casa.

• Miren las siguientes láminas. Pronuncien juntos cada letra y el nombre. Escuchen el sonido de la consonante al inicio de cada palabra.

f	m	s	t	h	b
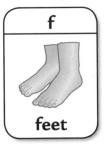		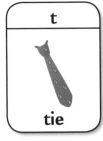			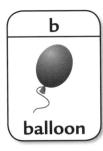
feet	**mirror**	**sun**	**tie**	**hand**	**balloon**

• Read the poem "Happy Birthday to Me!" on the reverse side of this page to your child.

• Talk about special ways your family celebrates birthdays.

• Find words in the poem that begin with **f, m, s, t, h,** and **b.** Also find words that rhyme. **(tree/me/be)**

• Lea al niño la poesía "Happy Birthday to Me!" en la página 21.

• Hable de la forma especial en que su familia celebra los cumpleaños.

• Busquen palabras en la poesía que comiencen con **f, m, s, t, h** y **b.** Busquen también palabras que rimen. **(tree/me/be)**

PROJECT

Your child may enjoy making a "My Family and Me" book. On a large piece of paper, have your child draw a self-portrait and label it **Me.** Work together to add pages for photos or drawings of family members. Attach the pages together with yarn or staples.

PROYECTO

Su niño puede divertirse haciendo un libro titulado, "Mi familia y yo". Pida al niño que se dibuje en un papel grande y escriba **yo** debajo. Añada hojas para fotos o dibujos de otros miembros de la familia. Sujete el libro con hilo o grapas.

 Visit us at **www.sadlierphonicsonline.com**

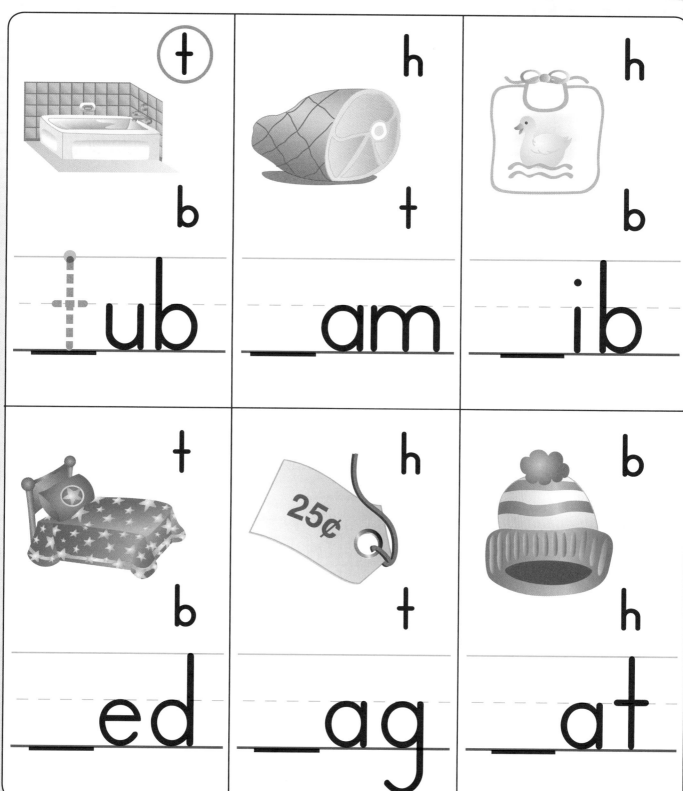

t
b
_t_ub

h
t
_am

h
b
_ib

t
b
_ed

h
t
_ag

b
h
_at

DIRECTIONS: Say the name of the picture. **Circle** the letter that stands for its beginning sound. **Print** the letter on the line to complete the picture name.

Pat

Bob

DIRECTIONS: **Pat** ends with **/t/. Bob** ends with **/b/.** At the top, **color** the picture if its name ends with the same sound as **Pat.** At the bottom, **color** the picture if its name ends with the same sound as **Bob.**

PHONICS ALIVE AT HOME

Say the names of family members. Talk about the sound at the end of each name.

Name_____

These words are often used in sentences.

| for | is | me | The |

1. ___The___ is for me.

2. The ___is___ for me.

3. The  is ___for___ me.

4. Is the  for ___me___?

 Read

DIRECTIONS: **Read** the words in the box. **Say** and **trace** the dotted word in each sentence. **Read** the sentences aloud.

1. The  _____ for me.

is

2. The 📖 is _____ me.

for

3. The ☀ is for _____ .

me

4. Is _____ for me?

the

 Check-Up

☺ the   ☺ for   ☺ is   ☺ me

DIRECTIONS: Print the word in the box on the line. **Read** the sentences.
Then **color** a smiley face for each word you wrote.

 PHONICS ALIVE AT HOME Have your child use the words in the Check-Up box to make up sentences that tell about places or things he or she likes.

Name _____

f	m	s
t	h	b
f	s	m
h	t	b

DIRECTIONS: **Say** the name of the picture. **Color** the picture if its name begins with the sound of the letter in the box.

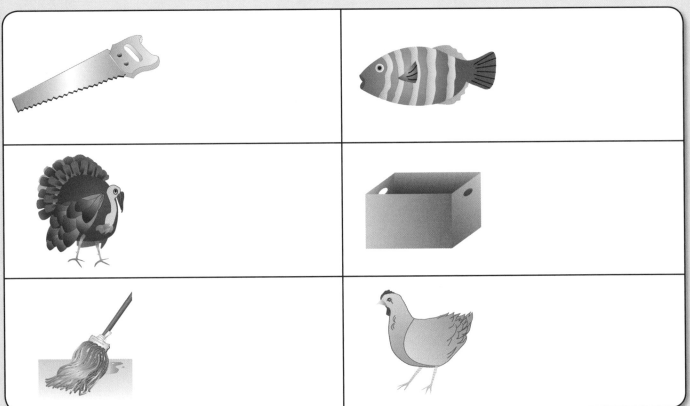

f   m   s   t   h   b

DIRECTIONS: **Cut out** the boxes at the bottom of the page. **Say** the name of the picture and **listen** for its beginning sound. **Glue** the letter that stands for its beginning sound next to the picture.

Name_____

READ ALOUD

Learn About a Special Game

Have you ever played
the Mexican piñata game
on your birthday?
The piñata is filled
with toys and party favors.
First you put on a blindfold.
Then you hit the piñata with a stick.
Wow!

DIRECTIONS: **Look** at the picture. **Listen** as the page is read aloud. What happens when you hit a piñata with a stick? Does breaking open a piñata look like fun?

Lesson 29 • Initial Consonants **f, m, s, t, h, b** in Context
Comprehension: Understanding Cause and Effect
Modeling Fluency

55

Happy Birthday to Me!

Time to Write

DIRECTIONS: Imagine the best birthday present ever. **Draw** a picture of your present in the box. **Write** what it is on the line.

PHONICS ALIVE AT HOME Pretend it is your child's birthday. Together, sing "Happy Birthday to You."

Name_____

Check-Up DIRECTIONS: **Say** the name of each picture. **Color** the picture if its name begins with the sound of the letter at the beginning of the row.

h

s

m

f

b

t

⭐ **Check-Up** DIRECTIONS: **Say** the name of the picture. **Draw** a line from the picture to its beginning sound.

 PHONICS ALIVE AT HOME Have your child say the sound that begins each picture name.

Reading at Home: Read the story together and listen for words that begin with **f, m, s, t, h,** and **b.** Then talk about the ways members of your family are the same and different.

Name _____

Who Do I Look Like?

Fold

Do I look like my sister?

1

Do I look like my twin brother?
No! He looks like me.

4

DIRECTIONS: Remove the page and fold.

Lesson 32 • Unit 2 Take-Home Book
Comprehension: Comparing and Contrasting

2

Do I look like my father?

Fold

Do I look like my mother?

3

WORK

My grandpa works in the garden.
My brother works in a store.
My daddy works in a restaurant.
My grandma works next door.

My mother works in an office.
My uncle works on cars.
I dreamed last night I went to work—
I went to work on Mars!

Babs Bell Hajdusiewicz

Oral Language Where would you like to work when you grow up?
Would you like to work on another planet? Why or why not?

Name _____

Dear Family,

In this unit about workers and their jobs, your child will learn the sounds of the consonants **l, d, c, n, g,** and **w.** You can help phonics come alive at home by trying these activities together.

- Look at the pictures below. Say each letter and picture name with your child. Listen to the beginning consonant sound in each word.

Apreciada Familia:

En esta unidad, que trata de los trabajadores y sus oficios, su niño aprenderá el sonido de las consonantes **l, d, c, n, g** y **w.** Puede ayudar a revivir los fonemas haciendo juntos las siguientes actividades:

- Miren los dibujos. Pronuncien cada letra y el nombre de las cosas. Escuchen el sonido de la consonante al inicio de cada palabra.

l	d	c	n	g	w

- Read the poem "Work" on the reverse side of this page to your child.
- Talk about jobs family members have.
- Find words in the poem that begin with **l, d, c, n, g,** and **w.** Also find rhyming words. **(store/door, cars/Mars)**

- Lea a su niño la poesía "Work" en la página 61.
- Hablen sobre los trabajos de los familiares.
- Busquen, en la poesía, palabras que comiencen con **l, d, c, n, g** y **w.** Busquen también palabras que rimen. **(store/door, cars/Mars)**

PROJECT

With your child, cut out pictures of workers from magazines or newspapers. Paste the pictures on a piece of paper and label them **doctor, waiter,** and so on. Circle the letters **l, d, c, n, g,** and **w** in your words.

PROYECTO

Con su niño, recorten de revistas o periódicos, láminas de trabajadores. Peguen las láminas en una hoja de papel. Ayude al niño a escribir el oficio de cada trabajador. Encierren en un círculo las letras **l, d, c, n, g** y **w** en cada palabra.

  Visit us at **www.sadlierphonicsonline.com**

Name _____

Workers at Work

Look! You can see workers at work.

Fold

Day and night, workers are at work.

4

These workers keep us safe.

Fold

These workers keep us healthy.

Yellow Butter

Yellow butter purple jelly red jam black bread

Spread it thick
Say it quick

Yellow butter purple jelly red jam black bread

Spread it thicker
Say it quicker

Yellow butter purple jelly red jam black bread

Now repeat it
While you eat it

Yellow butter purple jelly red jam black bread

Don't talk
With your mouth full!

Mary Ann Hoberman

Oral Language

What flavor jelly or jam do you like best?
What else do you spread on your bread?

Name _____

Dear Family,

In this unit, your child will learn the sounds of the consonants **p, r, k, j, q(u), v, y,** and **z**. Your child will also be learning about different kinds of food. You may wish to try these activities together at home.

- Read the poem "Yellow Butter" on the reverse side of this page to your child.

- Talk about the kinds of bread and kinds of spreads you eat.

- Chant the poem with your child again and again. Try to say it faster and faster.

- Together, find words in the poem that begin with some of the consonants below.

Apreciada Familia:

En esta unidad su niño aprenderá los sonidos de las consonantes **p, r, k, j, q(u), v, y,** y **z**. Su niño también aprenderá acerca de las diferentes comidas. Pueden hacer las siguientes actividades en casa.

- Lea a su niño la poesía "Yellow Butter" en la página 101.

- Hablen de los diferentes tipos de pan y mantequilla que comen.

- Entone la poesía junto con el niño una y otra vez. Pronúncienlas más y más rápido.

- Juntos busquen palabras en el poema que empiecen con las siguientes consonantes:

prkjqvyz

PROJECT

Print the letters **P, R, K, J, Q, V, Y,** and **Z** on cards. With your child, search the labels on food packages in your home. Ask your child to hold up the right card for each product name that begins with one of the letters. What other beginning letters do you see in words on food packages? It might be fun to try this game while grocery shopping together.

PROYECTO

Escriban las letras **P, R, K, J, Q, V, Y,** y **Z** en tarjetas. Busque etiquetas de paquetes de comida en la casa. Pida al niño que tome la tarjeta correcta para cada producto cuyo nombre empiece con una de las letras. ¿Qué otras letras iniciales ve en las palabras de los paquetes de comida? Sería divertido jugar este juego cuando van de compras.

Name _____

READ ALOUD

Learn About Bread

Bread for sale!
Just look at all the kinds
you can pick from.
What would you like?

Rye, wheat, or pan bread,
black, brown, or round bread,
fat, thin, or very long bread—
Quick, get it while it's hot!

DIRECTIONS: **Look** at the pictu[re]. **Listen** as the page is read aloud. What other foods come in these colors and sha[pes]?

Lesson 7 • Initial Consonants **p, r, k, j, q(u), v, y, z** in Context
Comprehension: Classifying Objects
Modeling Fluency

135

What Do You Like?

DIRECTIONS: What do you like to eat? Prepare your favorite meal.
Draw what you would eat. **Write** a sentence about it.

Have your child describe the meal he or she has prepared.

Name_____

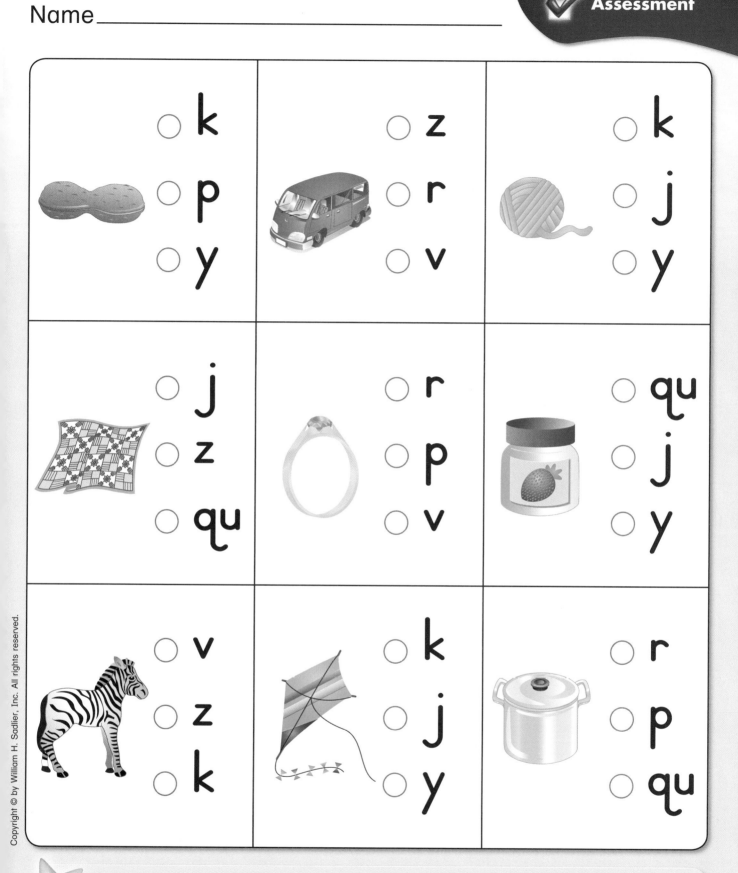

○ k
○ p
○ y

○ z
○ r
○ v

○ k
○ j
○ y

○ j
○ z
○ qu

○ r
○ p
○ v

○ qu
○ j
○ y

○ v
○ z
○ k

○ k
○ j
○ y

○ r
○ p
○ qu

Check-Up DIRECTIONS: **Say** the name of the picture. **Fill in** the circle next to the letter or letters that stand for the beginning sound.

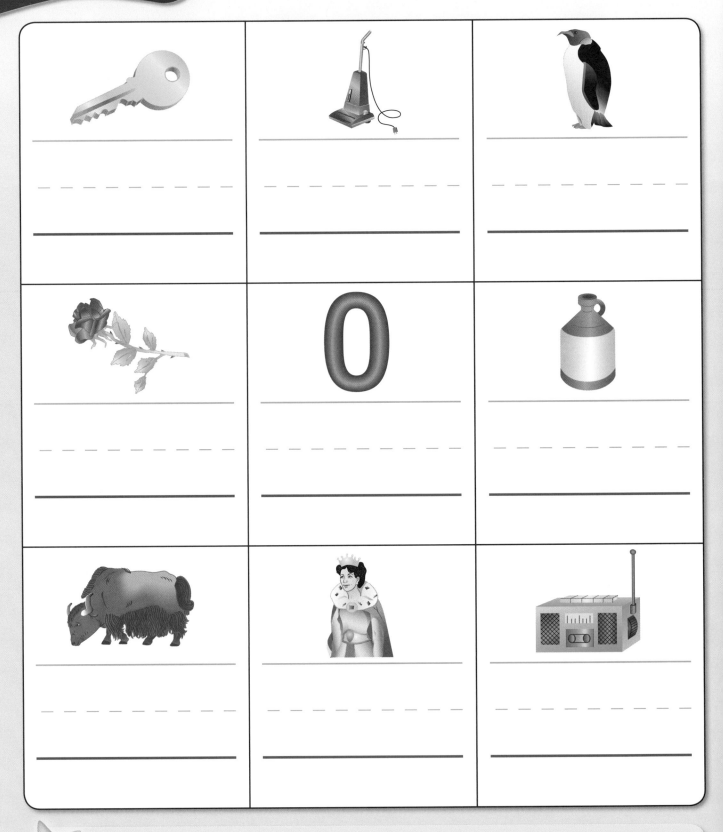

Lesson 73 • Assessing Initial Consonants
p, r, k, j, q(u), v, y, z

⭐
Check-UP DIRECTIONS: **Say** the name of the picture. **Write** the letter or letters that stand for its beginning sound on the line.

PHONICS
ALIVE AT HOME

Say the beginning sound of a picture name and have your child point to the picture that has that beginning sound.

Name _____

What's for Dinner?

What's for dinner?
Van is having rice.

—Fold—

Yummy!

What's for dinner?
You decide!

4

⋆ **DIRECTIONS:** Remove the page and fold.

Lesson 74 • Unit 4 Take-Home Book
Comprehension: Summarizing a Story

139

1

What's for dinner?
Zack is having pizza.

— Fold —

What's for dinner?
Kim is having tacos.

Lesson 74 • Unit 4 Take-Home Book
Comprehension: Summarizing a Story

Jump or Jiggle

Frogs jump
Caterpillars hump

Worms wiggle
Bugs jiggle

Rabbits hop
Horses clop

Snakes slide
Sea gulls glide

Mice creep
Deer leap

Puppies bounce
Kittens pounce

Lions stalk—
But—
I walk!

Evelyn Beyer

Oral Language What are different ways you can move?
How do your favorite animals move?

Name _____

Dear Family,

In this unit, your child will learn the sounds of the short vowels and also how people and animals move. As your child progresses through this unit, try these activities at home.

- Look at the pictures below. Say each letter and picture name with your child. Listen to the vowel sound in each word.

Apreciada Familia:

En esta unidad su niño aprenderá los sonidos cortos de las vocales y como se mueven la gente y los animales. A medida que el niño avanza, hagan estas actividades en casa.

- Miren juntos los siguientes dibujos. Pronuncien cada letra y el nombre del objeto. Escuchen el sonido de la vocal en cada palabra.

a	i	o	u	e
	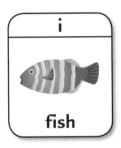			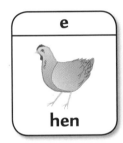
cat	fish	frog	duck	hen

- Read the poem "Jump or Jiggle" on the reverse side of this page to your child.

- Talk about ways that animals move.

- Read the poem aloud again. Pause before the last word in each stanza so that your child can supply the rhyming word.

- Together, find short vowel words in the poem, for example, **frogs, jump, wiggle, rabbits,** and **hop.**

- Lea al niño la poesía "Jump or Jiggle" en la página 141.

- Hablen de las formas en que los animales se mueven.

- De nuevo lea la poesía en voz alta. Haga pausa antes de la última palabra en cada estrofa para que el niño diga la palabra que rima.

- Busquen, en la poesía, palabras con vocales de sonido corto como: **frogs, jump, wiggle, rabbits** y **hop.**

PROJECT

PROYECTO

With your child, take turns acting out the ways a **crab, chimp, frog, duck,** and **hen** move. Help your child repeat the vowel sound in each animal name.

Túrnense para dramatizar el movimiento de los diferentes animales: cangrejos, monos, sapos, patos, gallinas. Ayude a su niño a repetir las vocales en el nombre del animal.

Visit us at **www.sadlierphonicsonline.com**

Name_____

c a t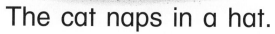

The cat naps in a hat.

b a g

c a n

m a p

 DIRECTIONS: **Trace** the line as you blend the sounds together to say the word. **Circle** the picture for the word.

c a p

c a b

j a m

m a p

v a n

b a t

DIRECTIONS: **Trace** the line as you blend the sounds together to say the word.
Circle the picture it names.

PHONICS ALIVE AT HOME

Name a picture on the page with the short **a** sound, and have your child find the word and blend its sounds.

Decodable Reader

Name _____

Cat at Bat

The cat had a bag.

1

Fold

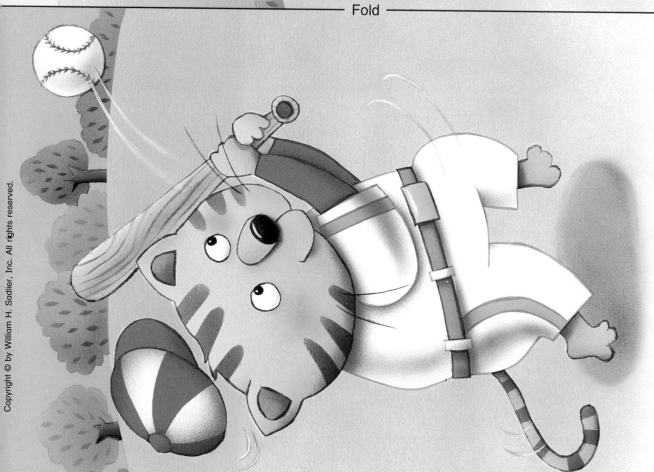

Bam!

4

DIRECTIONS: Cut and fold the book. Then read the story. Tell the story in your own words.

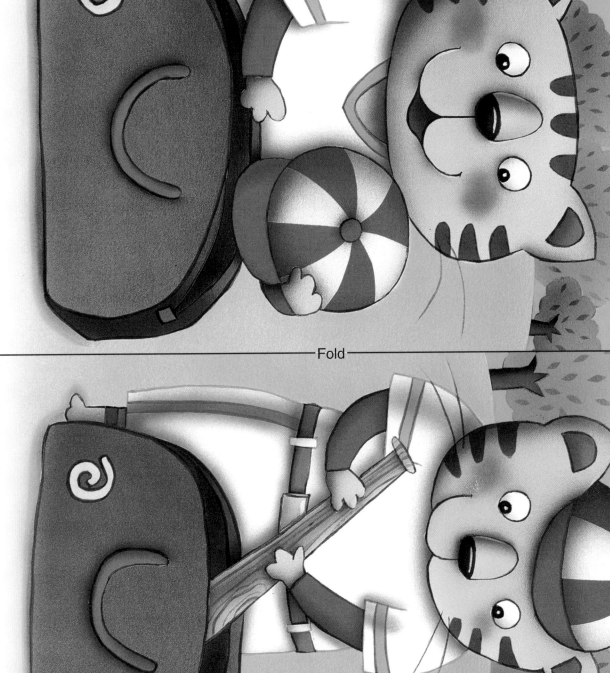

2

The cat had a cap.

Fold

The cat had a bat.

3

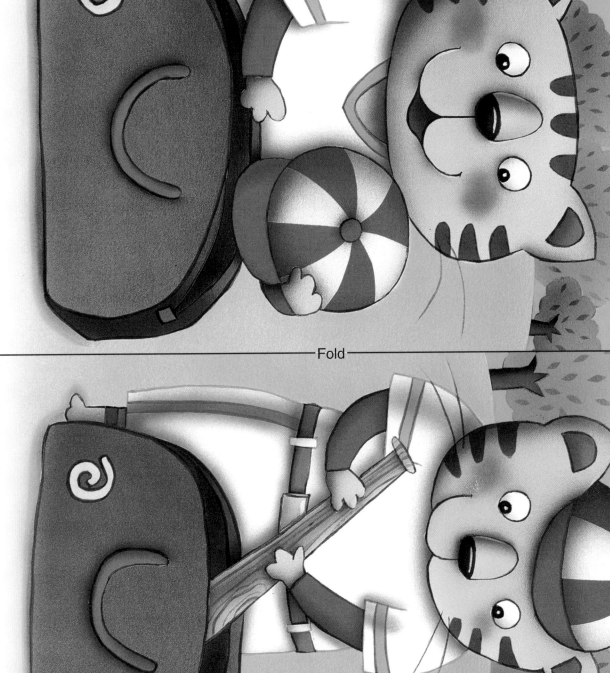

Lesson 79 • Short Vowel **a** Decodable Reader
Comprehension: Retelling a Story

Name_____

The cat ran.
I ran.

The cat sat.
I sat.

The cat had ham.
I had ham.

The cat can nap.
Can I?

DIRECTIONS: **Read** the sentences. **Draw** a picture about what you read.

Oh, That Bat!

| bat | jam | had | pan | bag | mad |

DIRECTIONS: What did the naughty bat do? **Write** about it. Use some short **a** words. **Look** at the words in the box if you need help.

With your child, look through storybooks to find short **a** words. Write a list of the words.

Name_____

DIRECTIONS: **Say** the name of each picture. **Circle** the picture whose name has the short **a** sound. **Print a** on the line.

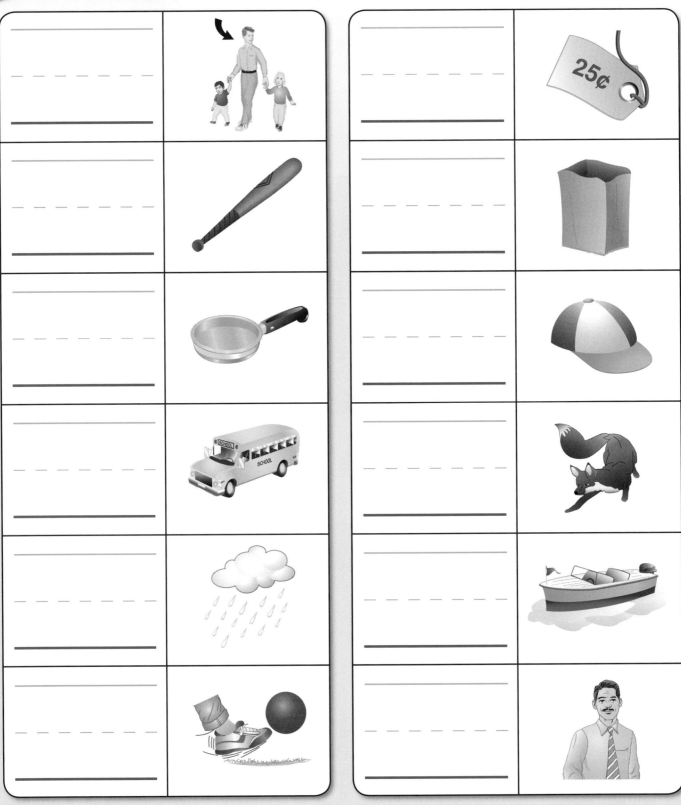

DIRECTIONS: **Say** the name of the picture. If the picture name has the short **a** sound, **print a** on the line.

PHONICS
ALIVE AT HOME

Point to a picture and ask your child to say its name. If the picture name has the short **a** sound, have your child clap.

Ilsa fills the bin.

DIRECTIONS: **Bin** has the short **i** sound. **Say** the name of each picture.
Draw a line to the bin if the picture name has the short **i** sound.

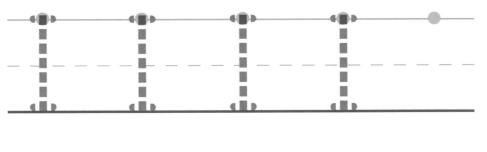

Iggy Iguana

DIRECTIONS: **Name, trace,** and **print** the letters **I** and **i.** In each row, find the iguana that has the same letter as the green iguana. **Color** that iguana green.

Have your child point to and name the letter on each iguana.

Name_____

DIRECTIONS: **Say** the name of the picture. If the picture name has the short **i** sound, **print i** on the line.

Pick a bib for Pig!

- ○ a
- ○ i
- ○ e

- ○ o
- ○ a
- ○ i

- ○ i
- ○ u
- ○ o

- ○ i
- ○ e
- ○ a

- ○ u
- ○ i
- ○ o

- ○ e
- ○ a
- ○ i

DIRECTIONS: Say the name of the picture. If the picture name has the short **i** sound, **fill in** the bubble next to the **i**.

Phonemic Awareness: /i/
Connecting Sound to Symbol: /i/ **i**

PHONICS
ALIVE AT HOME

Ask your child to name other words he or she knows with the sound of short **i**. Together, make a list of the words and add to it as your child thinks of more.

Name_____

A pig can dig.

p i g

b i b

f i n

k i t

DIRECTIONS: **Trace** the line as you blend the sounds together to say the word.
Circle the picture for the word.

d i g

f i n

p i n

r i p

s i x

p i g

DIRECTIONS: **Trace** the line as you blend the sounds together to say the word.
Circle the picture it names.

PHONICS ALIVE AT HOME
Ask your child to circle the letter in each word that makes the short **i** sound.

Name _____

Pig in a Wig

A wig

— Fold —

A pig in a wig did a jig.

4

DIRECTIONS: Cut and fold the book. Then read the story. Tell what happens after the pig sees the wig.

Lesson 85 • Short Vowel **i** Decodable Reader
Comprehension: Sequencing

A pig

Fold

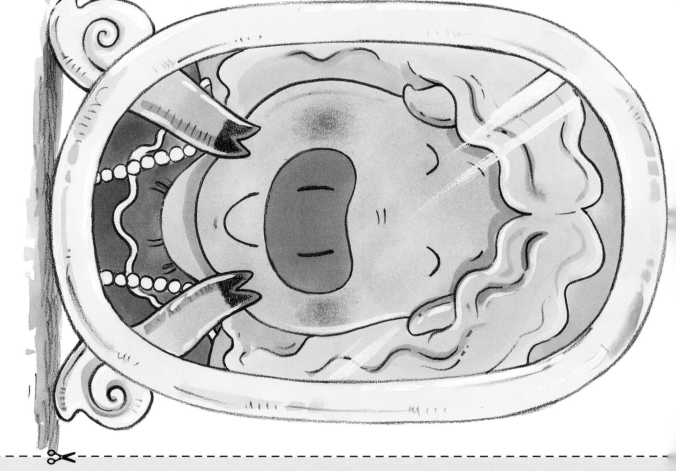

A pig in a wig

2

3

Can a pig sit?
It can!

Can you sit?
You can!

Can a pig dig?
It can!

Can you dig?
You can!

DIRECTIONS: **Read** the sentences. **Draw** a picture about what you read.

Fish swim to win!

FINISH

1st

| fish | win | will | it | swim | fin |

1st

DIRECTIONS: Which fish will win the race? **Write** about it. Use some short **i** words.
Look at the words in the box if you need help.

PHONICS ALIVE AT HOME

With your child, look in newspapers or magazines to find short **i** words. Write a list of the words.

Name _____

A Wet Hen

A wet hen

— Fold —

A wet me!

4

DIRECTIONS: Cut and fold the book. Then read the story. Tell why the hen, cat, dog, and child get wet.

Lesson 104 • Short Vowel **e** Decodable Reader
Comprehension: Understanding
Cause and Effect

199

2

A wet cat

Fold

A wet dog

3

Lesson 104 • Short Vowel e Decodable Reader
Comprehension: Understanding Cause and Effect

This is Ted.
Ted is not my pet yet.

I can get a net.
I can get Ted with a net.

This is my pet, Meg.
I got Meg with a net.

I like Meg.
I like Ted.

DIRECTIONS: **Read** the sentences. **Draw** a picture about what you read.

Ten Red Hens

ten	hens	pen	nest	legs	red

DIRECTIONS: What are all of these hens doing? **Write** about them. Use some short **e** words. **Look** at the words in the box if you need help.

PHONICS ALIVE AT HOME

With your child, look in storybooks to find short **e** words. Write a list of the words you find.

Name_____

DIRECTIONS: **Print e** at the beginning of the row. **Say** the name of each picture.
Circle the picture if its name has the short **e** sound.

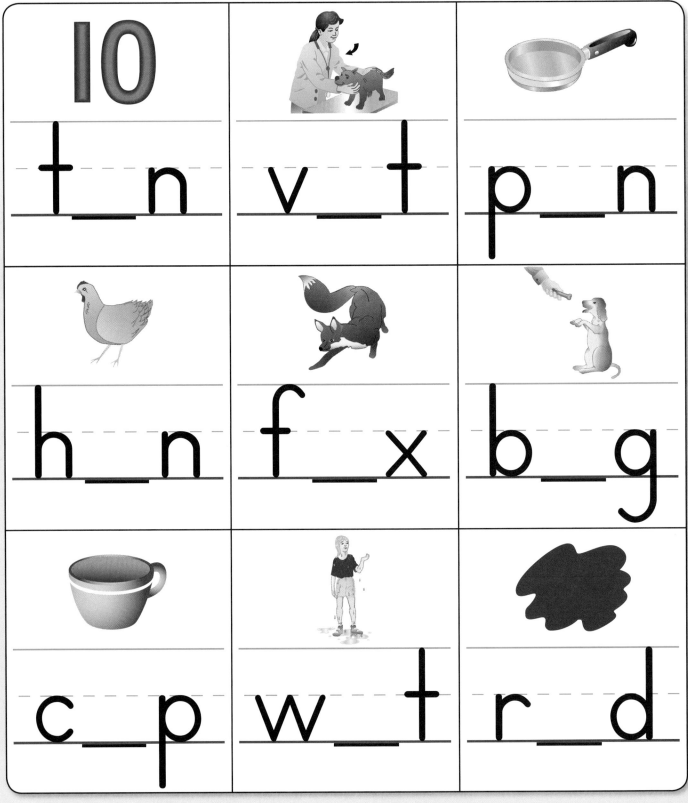

10

t _ n

v _ t

p _ n

h _ n

f _ x

b _ g

c _ p

w _ t

r _ d

DIRECTIONS: **Say** the name of the picture. If the picture name has the short **e** sound, **print e** on the line.

PHONICS
ALIVE AT HOME

Call out the short **e** words to your child and have him or her say a rhyming word.

Name_____

These words are often used in sentences.

jump   run   So   too

1. A  can ___run___.

2. ___So___ can I.

3. A  can ___jump___.

4. I can jump, ___too___.

DIRECTIONS: **Read** the words in the box. **Say** and **trace** the dotted word in each sentence. **Read** the sentences aloud.

Visit **www.sadlierphonicsonline.com** to do this activity online.

1. I _____ get fit!

| | can |

2. I can _____ with my .

| | jump |

3. I can jump _____ my 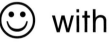.

| | with |

4. Can you jump, _____?

| | too |

☺ too   ☺ jump   ☺ run   ☺ can

☺ so   ☺ not   ☺ that   ☺ with

DIRECTIONS: **Print** the word in the box on the line. **Read** the sentences.
Then **color** a smiley face for each word you wrote.

PHONICS ALIVE AT HOME

Use chalk to print each word in the Check-Up box on the sidewalk. Have your child jump from word to word, reading each word as he or she lands on it.

Name_____

Learn About Our Legs

Our legs do lots of jobs.
We use them to walk, kick, hop, and jump.
We use them to dance, too.

We can bend our legs because they have joints.
Joints are like hinges on a door.
Without knee joints, we couldn't move well.
Keep your legs stiff and try to run.
What happens?

DIRECTIONS: **Look** at the pictures. **Listen** as the page is read aloud. What happens when you try to run with stiff knees? What other joints help you to move?

Lesson 108 • Short Vowels in Context
Modeling Fluency
Comprehension: Recognizing Facts

Fun in the Sun

dad	dig	hot	fun	get	wet

DIRECTIONS: What can you do to have fun in the sun? **Write** about it. Use some short **a**, short **i**, short **o**, short **u**, and short **e** words. **Look** at the words in the box if you need help.

PHONICS ALIVE AT HOME

With your child, go for a walk outside to find things with short vowel names. Write a list of the words that name what you find.

Name _____

mop mat	6 sad six	bib bug
leg beg	hat sat	cap can
nut net	dig dog	pin pan

Check-UP DIRECTIONS: **Say** the name of the picture. **Circle** the picture name.
Print the name on the line.

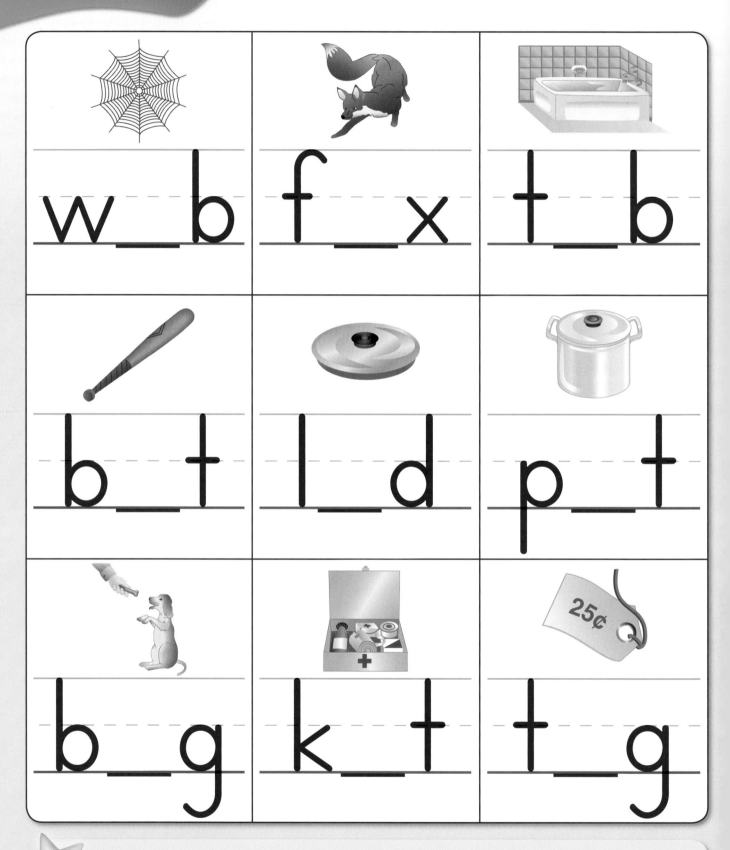

w _ b   f _ x   t _ b

b _ t   l _ d   p _ t

b _ g   k _ t   t _ g

Check-UP DIRECTIONS: Say the name of the picture. **Print** the letter that stands for the vowel sound to complete the picture name.

PHONICS ALIVE AT HOME   Have your child find a word on the page for each short vowel sound (a, i, o, u, e).

Name —————

At the Park

Kids sit and spin at the park.

Fold

What do you do at the park?

4

DIRECTIONS: Remove the page and fold.

2

Ducks splish and splash
at the park.

Fold

Men jog with dogs
at the park.

3

I Drew a Yellow Unicorn

I drew a yellow unicorn,
Complete with polka dots,
A seven-legged elephant,
A pig with purple spots.
The sky was full of furry fish
All flying upside down.
An octopus was dressed in plaid,
A camel wore a crown.

I drew a green rhinoceros
That floated on the breeze,
Some bees as big as basketballs,
And blue spaghetti trees.
The penguins wore pajamas,
And a carrot flew a kite . . . .
My teacher says it's beautiful—
I think my teacher's right.

Jack Prelutsky

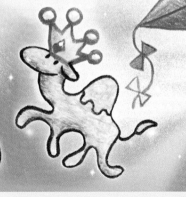

Oral Language Do you think any of these things could be real?
How is this girl's imagination like yours?

Lesson 112 • Long Vowels
Poetry: Imagery
Developing Fluency

213

Name _____

Dear Family,

In this unit about imagination, your child will learn the sounds of the long vowels. As your child progresses through this unit, you can try these activities together at home.

• Look at the pictures below. Say each letter and a picture name with your child. Listen for the long vowel sounds. (Long vowels say their own name.)

Apreciada Familia:

En esta unidad, su niño aprenderá los sonidos de las vocales de sonido largo. A medida que el niño avanza en esta unidad, hagan estas actividades en casa.

• Miren los siguientes dibujos. Pronuncien juntos las letras y el nombre del dibujo. Presten atención al sonido de las vocales de sonido largo. (Las vocales de sonido largo se pronuncian igual a como se llaman.)

a	i	o	u	e
		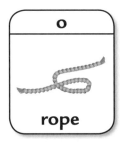	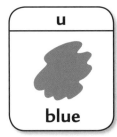	
cage	ride	rope	blue	bee

• Read the poem, "I Drew a Yellow Unicorn" on the reverse side of this page and talk about the animals in the poem.

• Help your child find long vowel words in the poem, such as **I, yellow, floated, unicorn, blue, green, breeze, bees, trees, kite,** and **right.** Also find words that rhyme. **(dots/spots, down/crown, breeze/trees, kite/right)**

• Lea la poesía "I Drew a Yellow Unicorn" al reverso de esta página y hablen sobre los animales de la poesía.

• Ayude al niño a buscar en la poesía palabras con vocales de sonido largo, como: **I, yellow, floated, unicorn, blue, green, breeze, bees, trees, kite,** y **right.** Busquen también palabras que rimen. **(dots/spots, down/crown, breeze/ trees, kite/right)**

PROJECT

Help your child recall all the animals that were described in the poem. Then ask your child to draw a picture of a unicorn. Ask him or her to color in the unicorn with crayons or markers whose colors have long vowels in their names. **(blue, green, white, yellow)**

PROYECTO

Ayude al niño a recordar todos los animales descritos en la poesía. Luego, pídale que dibuje un unicornio y que lo coloree con crayones o marcadores de colores que contengan, en el nombre, vocales de sonido largo. **(blue, green, white, yellow)**

 Visit us at **www.sadlierphonicsonline.com**

Name_____

Kate dresses up in a cape!

DIRECTIONS: **Cape** has the long **a** sound. **Say** the name of the picture.
Color the cape if the picture name has the long **a** sound.

Wake up, Jake!

tape

g t ___

v s ___

c p ___

r k ___

g m ___

w v ___

DIRECTIONS: **Say** the name of the picture. **Listen** for the long **a** sound and **print** the letters that stand for the sound.

216 Lesson 113 • Phonemic Awareness: /ā/
Connecting Sound to Symbol: /ā/ a_e

Have your child find and name all the objects on the page that have the sound of long **a** in their names.

Name _____

Mike is a fire fighter!

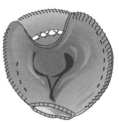

DIRECTIONS: **Mike** has the long **i** sound. **Say** the name of each picture.
Draw a line from the picture to Mike if the picture name has the long **i** sound.

Nine in line!

9

n i n e

DIRECTIONS: **Say** the name of the picture. **Listen** for the long **i** sound and
print the letters that stand for the sound.

Have your child find nine things in your
home that have the sound of long **i** in
their names.

Name_____

Moe hopes to find his bone.

DIRECTIONS: **Bone** has the long **o** sound. Help Moe find his bone. **Draw** a path through the maze. Follow the pictures whose names have the long **o** sound.

Rose follows her nose!

r o s e

b n   c n   h s

r b   n t   r p

DIRECTIONS: **Say** the name of the picture. **Listen** for the long **o** sound and
print the letters that stand for the sound.

**PHONICS
ALIVE AT HOME**

Help your child make up rhyming words
that have the long **o** sound in them. For
example, **bone/cone, hose/nose.**

DIRECTIONS: Say the name of the picture in the box. **Circle** the pictures whose names have the same long vowel sound as the picture in the box.

Review

c a p e   d _ m _   n _ t

g _ m _   d _ v _   w _ v _

r _ p _   b _ t _   h _ s _

DIRECTIONS: **Say** the name of the picture. **Listen** for the long vowel sound and **print** the letters that stand for the sound.

222 Lesson 116 • Reviewing Long Vowels **a, i, o**

 Point to a picture. Have your child name the word and spell it.

Name _____

Dave can ride
a bike.
I can, too.

Rose can run
a mile.
I can, too.

Mike can make
a kite.
I can, too.

Nate can jump
rope.
Can you?

DIRECTIONS: **Read** the sentences. **Draw** a picture about what you read.

A Home for Mole

| mole | hole | hide | bike | safe | cake |

DIRECTIONS: Where does Mole live? **Write** about it. Use some long **a**, long **i**, and long **o** words. **Look** at the words in the box if you need help.

PHONICS ALIVE AT HOME Have your child dictate a sentence to you about one of his or her stuffed animals. Encourage him or her to use long **a**, long **i**, and long **o** words.

June plays a tune.

DIRECTIONS: **Tune** has the long **u** sound. **Say** the name of each picture.
Color the picture blue if its name has the long **u** sound.

Five mules rule the band!

m u l e   c _ b _   d _ n _

J _ n _   t _ n _   t _ b _

DIRECTIONS: **Say** the name of the picture. **Listen** for the long **u** sound and **print** the letters that stand for the sound.

Lesson 118 • Phonemic Awareness: /o͞o/ and /yo͞o/
Connecting Sound to Symbol:
/o͞o/ and /yo͞o/ u_e

PHONICS ALIVE AT HOME

Point to one of the pictures on the page as you cover the letters. Ask your child to say and spell the name of the picture.

Name_____

What a tree I see!

DIRECTIONS: **Tree** has the long **e** sound. **Say** the name of each picture. If the picture name has the long **e** sound, **color** the space green. If the picture name does not have the long **e** sound, **color** the space brown.

Lesson 119 • Phonemic Awareness: /ē/

227

Beep! Beep! Here come three sheep.

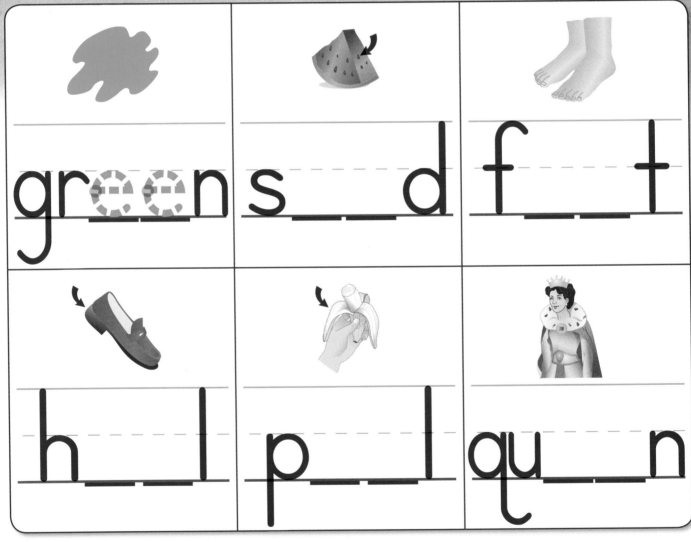

gr__ns   s__d   f__t

h__l   p__l   qu__n

DIRECTIONS: **Say** the name of the picture. **Listen** for the long **e** sound and
print the letters that stand for the sound.

Write the letters **ee** on a piece of paper.
Have your child add letters before and
after the **ee** to make new words.

Name_____

 These words are often used in sentences.

| one   too   have   what |

1. I  have five   .

2. I have 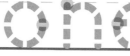 one  .

3. I have one  , too .

4. I like  what I have!

 DIRECTIONS: Read the words in the box. **Say** and **trace** the dotted word in each sentence. **Read** the sentences aloud.

 **Review**

1. I _____ one  .

   | have

2. I have _____  .

   | one

3. My  _____ run.

   | can

4. My  can _____ .

   | jump

 Check-Up

☺ have   ☺ not   ☺ one   ☺ can

☺ with   ☺ jump   ☺ are   ☺ what

DIRECTIONS: **Print** the word in the box on the line. **Read** the sentences.
Then **color** a smiley face for each word you wrote.

230 Lesson 120 • Reviewing High-Frequency Words

 PHONICS ALIVE AT HOME Have your child draw a picture of a pet. Work together to make up sentences about the pet using words from the Check-Up box.

Name_____

 DIRECTIONS: **Say** the name of the picture in the box. **Circle** the pictures whose names have the same long vowel sound as the picture in the box.

Take a ride!

n _ s _

v _ n _

r _ k _

qu _ n _

m _ l _

f _ t _

r _ d _

DIRECTIONS: **Say** the name of the picture. **Listen** for the long vowel sound and **print** the letters that stand for the sound.

PHONICS ALIVE AT HOME
Call out a long vowel. Ask your child to name a picture on the page that has that long vowel sound.

Name_____

READ ALOUD

Learn About Imagination

Most of us think of salad when we see fruit or vegetables on a plate. But some of us see more.
Some of us see a face with eyes, a nose, and a smile.
Some of us see a wagon.
And some of us even see a whole person!

Before you take a bite, look at your food. Use YOUR imagination. What do you see?

DIRECTIONS: **Look** at the pictures. **Listen** as the page is read aloud. What fruits and vegetables can you name?

Need a bone?

DEINONYCHUS

| like | June | need | bone | make | time |

DIRECTIONS: What is the woman in the museum doing? **Write** about it. Use some long **a, i, o, u,** and **e** words. **Look** at the words in the box if you need help.

PHONICS ALIVE AT HOME On a piece of paper, draw and cut out five dinosaur bones. Have your child write a long vowel word on each bone.

Name _____

f _ v   b _ n   c _ k

f _ _   t _ n   b _ k

w _ v   s _ d   r _ b

Check-Up DIRECTIONS: **Say** the name of the picture. **Listen** for the long vowel sound and **print** the letters that stand for the sound.

dime

tape

cake

feet

note

mule

bee

June

Check-Up ★ DIRECTIONS: **Say** the name of each picture. **Read** the word. **Fill in** the bubble next to the picture named.

PHONICS ALIVE AT HOME Point to a picture and have your child tell you a rhyming word.

Name _____

My Plane Ride

I ride in my plane for miles and miles.

— Fold —

I fly back home and go to sleep.
Sweet dreams!

2

I see huge white clouds above me.

I see huge green fields below me.

3

Name _____ Year 20____–20____

My Progress Checklist

 😊 **I need to practice this.**   ☺ **I know this.**

Unit 1: Phonological and Phonemic Awareness

○ ☺ Count words in a sentence
○ ☺ Recognize rhyming words
○ ☺ Recognize syllables
○ ☺ Recognize sounds in words
○ ☺ Match sounds in words
○ ☺ Recognize different sounds in groups of words
○ ☺ Blend sounds
○ ☺ Break words into separate sounds
○ ☺ Take away a sound in a word
○ ☺ Add a sound to a word
○ ☺ Change a sound in a word

The Alphabet

○ ☺ Aa, Bb, Cc, Dd, Ee, Ff
○ ☺ Gg, Hh, Ii, Jj, Kk, Ll
○ ☺ Mm, Nn, Oo, Pp, Qq, Rr
○ ☺ Ss, Tt, Uu, Vv, Ww, Xx, Yy, Zz

I need to practice this.   **I know this.**

Unit 2: Consonants

- ◯ ☺ f
- ◯ ☺ m
- ◯ ☺ s
- ◯ ☺ t
- ◯ ☺ h
- ◯ ☺ b

Unit 3: Consonants

- ◯ ☺ l
- ◯ ☺ d
- ◯ ☺ c
- ◯ ☺ n
- ◯ ☺ g
- ◯ ☺ w

Unit 4: Consonants

- ◯ ☺ p
- ◯ ☺ r
- ◯ ☺ k
- ◯ ☺ j
- ◯ ☺ q(u)
- ◯ ☺ v
- ◯ ☺ y
- ◯ ☺ z
- ◯ ☺ x

Unit 5: Short Vowels

- ◯ ☺ a
- ◯ ☺ i
- ◯ ☺ o
- ◯ ☺ u
- ◯ ☺ e

Unit 6: Long Vowels

- ◯ ☺ a
- ◯ ☺ i
- ◯ ☺ o
- ◯ ☺ u
- ◯ ☺ e

High-Frequency Words

- ◯ ☺ the
- ◯ ☺ is
- ◯ ☺ for
- ◯ ☺ me

- ◯ ☺ a
- ◯ ☺ be
- ◯ ☺ can
- ◯ ☺ I

- ◯ ☺ like
- ◯ ☺ you
- ◯ ☺ with
- ◯ ☺ do

- ◯ ☺ not
- ◯ ☺ that
- ◯ ☺ my
- ◯ ☺ this

- ◯ ☺ run
- ◯ ☺ jump
- ◯ ☺ so
- ◯ ☺ too

- ◯ ☺ have
- ◯ ☺ one
- ◯ ☺ are
- ◯ ☺ what